Reversing Heart Failure: Te Hope. From Patients with Di
Part 2

The Raw Vegan Plant-Based Detoxification & Regeneration Workbook for Healing Patients.

Volume 7

Health Central

Copyright © 2020

Topics Discussed & Journal Structure

1. Testimonials & Success Stories Continued

2. Our Story

3. Important Notes for Overcoming Your Heart Failure

4. The Power of Journaling

5. Daily Journal Examples

6. 30 Day Assisted Journal Section

Testimonials & Success Stories Continued

In the last volume we presented you with a series of testimonials and success stories from patients that have endured a variety of conditions and overcame them through the use of the raw vegan (high fruit and some vegetables) regimen that we have discussed over the different volumes in this series.

Our aim was to give you hope because we realise that sometimes we all need some encouragement and reinforcement on our healing journeys. Sometimes we are just lost and unsure where to turn. Hopefully we are helping and supporting you by sharing these success stories.

In this volume, we will continue to share more success stories from patients that overcame a variety of ailments. The key is to take note of the healing protocol that they all have in common.

If you have a success story to share or even if you are experiencing any type of improvement as a result of applying the information that we have shared in this series, please do feel free to send us your story – we would love to hear from you: **healingcentral8@gmail.com**

We welcome your success stories and they inspire us to continue to work even harder in order to get this message out there.

Success Story #5: Hashimoto Autoimmune Disease – Ovarian Tumour – Hair Loss

"Hello,

I would like to share with you the wonderful results I achieved thanks to this lifestyle and following this fruit diet.

This testimony is about hair loss and the wonderful results I have gained.

How after 6 years of extreme hair loss I did what I was told by medical doctors that will be impossible: I grew my hair back! Naturally! And the results have exceeded my expectations.

I was told that I had female pattern hair loss, I've also had many endocrine issues- adrenal and thyroid (Hashimoto), ovarian tumor, endometriosis, severe anemia, etc. I had so much radiation to my head and other many things that could have been linked/ responsible for the hair loss.

I began to lose hair in my early 20's. Every day I was losing so much hair. Every day for 6 years.

My scalp was burning! It was red and very painful to touch. My hair falling got worse, even my body hair began to fall. I was in so much pain that I couldn't sleep for days. I was in Hell.

At the beginning of the year 2015 I started to use herbs and tinctures.

In January 2015 I started this high fruit and some herbs regimen.

In the summer of 2015 I noticed some new fine, thin hairs beginning to grow back. At that point my hair was growing and falling at the same time, even the new ones.

In January 2016 I decided that I will regain my health and get my life back.

I began to have a positive mental attitude, faith and confidence that I will be successful.

In January to February of 2016 I changed my hair care routine and products and started using only Morocco Method Int'l. I've began using the scalp massager and following the recommendations of cutting my hair every month following the Lunar hair chart.

I believe that this combination of raw foods, fruits, different types of fasting, tinctures (especially for the Upper Circulation and Brain and Nerve), Morrocco Method products (especially the scalp massager), having faith, confidence that I will be successful and cultivating a positive mental attitude made wonders for my hair and overall well being.

My hair began to grow so fast, it began to get thicker and the hair fall almost stopped completely!

Some of my hair used to be so thin that if I took a single hair and placed it on a white sheet of paper, it would have been almost invisible.

Before my hair began to fall, I used to dye it for about 7-8 years. Through the years I used to dye my hair with tints of red, golden brown and dark brown. I stopped dying my hair in 2010 (because of the hair loss).

After I went vegan in 2013 I've noticed that my natural hair started to have a brown- reddish color.

Well, when it began to grow, in 2016…it grew a light brown-golden color! In about 6 months I had an incredible amount of hair on my scalp!!! My hair continued to grow this golden color for several months.

My hair kept getting stronger and thicker and continued to grow all over my body.

After a while my hair stopped growing this golden color and it began to grow a very dark brown.

Right now I have 3 different natural nuances in my hair. Everyone thinks my hair is dyed. I've had two theories regarding my hair growing a golden color:

1. At first I thought that maybe my hair should have been blonde from the beginning.

Since my father as a child had blonde, curly hair and later in life changed to dark brown- black.

2. The second theory is that the portion of my hair that grew golden brown was due to the color that I used to dye my hair with. When my hair began to grow blonde I thought that they will continue to grow like this for the rest of my life, but after some months it started to grow a very dark brown (my natural hair color as a child).

My scalp in not hurting anymore, the extreme itchiness is gone, the redness is gone, the burning is gone.

Now I can concentrate more, I can think, I am more awake, more aware, the brain fog is gone and I'm beginning to feel more like myself every day.

I am full of enthusiasm when I see how my hair is growing, so long and so fast.

Every day while combing my hair I am amazed to see the short hairs that keep growing among the long hairs. It is incredible!

I hope that this testimony will give hope to people who suffer from hair loss and also other ailments.

I never could accept the medical doctors sentence. I've always felt it in my heart that I will regrow my hair, despite the odds.

My own mother tried to comfort me, kept telling me to resign myself, to give up, to accept that I will not grow my hair back and to stop trying because is not the end of the world and that are many women in the world living just fine without hair. No one believed that it was possible. I proved them all wrong.

The opinions of other people do not have to become your reality. Believe you can heal and you will, sooner or later.

With love."

Success Story #6: Uterus Cancer

Back in 2011, I went back to the ER because my bladder was blocked. This is where I understood the cause - I had a tumour of the size of a cantaloupe melon. After cleaning my bladder, the doctor gave me several tests. They told me I had uterus cancer, and that I needed a hysterectomy and chemotherapy. However, I had been told that these two things will only increase my life hope for 1-2 years, and that I would also need to take hormones.

I told the doctors that they can only remove the tumour without touching my organs, including my uterus. They told me that I was crazy. They shook their heads and shirred their eyebrows. They called a psychiatrist to evaluate me. I told the doctors that I was going to sue them if i left the hospital missing organs. They wanted me to sign forms, but I refused to sign it all. I gave them the permission verbally to remove only the part of the tumour and nothing else.

After leaving the hospital, I started a fruit and leafy green juice diet. I drank fruit, and also green juices 6-8 times a day, I made enemas with water and wheat grass. When I came back to New York City two months later, I had a consultation with an oncologist and a gynaecologist. They told me that my cancer was almost gone. I continued this diet and protocol. When I went back to see the oncologist 5 months after my diagnosis, he told me that the cancer was completely gone and there was no trace of the disease anymore!

To cure my cancer, I had to stop eating meat, eggs, milk, cheese, yogurt and all the other forms of animal protein / fats.

My current diet:

- 50 % Raw Fruit

- 50 % Raw Vegetables (the leaves and the roots)

- I eat cooked foods only in winter

- I don't eat anything that comes from a tin can.

The key that allowed me to leave my cancer and stay healthy has been to switch to a living, raw and plant-based diet.

In 2016, I started to eat organic meat. After a few months, I immediately felt that something was wrong, so I stopped.

5 years after my healing, I look back in fascination that I went through this ordeal.

Success Story #7: Brain Cancer (French to English Translation)

"3 years ago, my life changed. I had a brain surgery and I was diagnosed with a stage 3 Anaplastic Astrocytoma, a rare type of brain cancer. A terminal cancer.

I refused chemo and radiation (what they call "treatments") because for me it was nonsense to take them while I had already been told that I was "incurable". I was supposed to die at the end of the treatment in any case, then why would I let them poison my body?

The doctor said it would make my life 2 or 3 years old, but the tumour would probably come back more aggressive. So I said no! So they told me that I only have 6 months left to live. I refused to believe them and I started my own research. This is when I discovered the raw vegan method of healing. I started to eat alive, raw fruit and vegetables.

This is the best decision I've ever made. God led me to this path and I know it. 3 years later I'm not only still alive, but 99 % of my symptoms have disappeared! I've never felt such good health. I am so grateful for this second chance at life. I love my life and I'll do everything to get the best out of it every day.

Thank you to all my friends who were in this journey with me. I love you all."

Success Story #8: Ovary Cyst

"The results are in !!!!!

I HAD a mass/cyst in my left ovary. I have been eating raw since October 2018 with the occasional slip up.

I started this protocol strictly in November 2018 and did an extended grape juice fast to start with.

I went for an ultra sound last week because my doctor was trying to scare me into surgery. And yesterday I got the results of that ultrasound.

THE MASS IS GONE

My ovaries are completely normal in size and show nothing abnormal.

I thank God for giving me the wisdom and the fruits to heal my body. Thank you for the truth. Thank you to all of my accountability partners during the grape juice fasts. I couldn't have done it without you!!!"

Success Story #9: Diabetes - Hypothyroidism

"I reversed the following: Diabetes, Acidosis, Hypothyroidism, Cholesterol, Migraines, Insomnia, Neck Pain.

Allopathic medicines didn't help me for 8 years.

I learnt about the raw foods, plant-based diet and I very quickly noticed that I was feeling the best I had ever felt. Everything started to normalize within 2-3 weeks and I threw away all allopathic synthetic poisons which gave me bad side effects. I had been taking 10 tablets every day.

On the fruit regimen I lost 10 kg of extra weight to become 60 kg with a perfect BMI of 22 for my height.

Quit all animals based, wheat, white rice, oils and all processed crap and I still ate beautifully. In my 6+ months vegan journey, I am almost an organic fruitarian now with some exceptions of steamed cooked vegetables.

Nature created us and nature had the cure, but in all honesty, if we all lived by nature and ate the diet intended for us, things like disease wouldn't exist.

Go back to nature. Go raw vegan, live a compassionate and healthy life."

Success Story #10: Kidney Failure - Irritable Bowel Syndrome

"I hope my story can serve as a reminder to others that no matter what, when you keep moving forward, no matter how slowly, you WILL get there.

I know some people struggle to know if they will ever heal. I GET IT. I was there, but realize that HEALING IS POSSIBLE! YES IT IS!

Why I did what I did? What got me here? What's my story? These are things I hear frequently.

Well, 1st off my story is long! I will try to condense it as much as I can. I struggled with gut issues since around junior high from what I remember. Skin issues as well of course. Then in highschool gut issues progressed and they labeled me IBS (because this is a label the medical field likes to use to encompass things they don't understand or cannot diagnose), I didn't fit in a category. Then it was hormonal issues with excruciatingly painful periods and irregular cycles. So what do you think is next?? YEP a pill. Not, lets address the WHY, lets cover it up and you'll never know what is really wrong then but you'll keep coming back for those meds. Yep yep, those meds that don't cure a thing but are very profitable.

So I kept going along as long as I had that pill. I was fairly OK. While in highschool I dealt with anxiety and lack of concentration and retention of information. I fought through anxiety by studying ALL the time, it's all I did just because I was so worried about passing because of my lack of retaining info.

Then came college in my senior year of highschool (which i have no idea how with my lack of retention), but as I got into the couple years of it, my anxiety and stress was through the roof and I remember just losing it and my mom being like "ok this is enough we are getting you tested". I was all for it because I just wanted answers. So I was tested and sure enough I had pretty major issues on my brain connecting things together. Now I knew why I hated to read so badly. It was exhausting, but did this really get addressing the ROOT causes however? No.

I got married, moved away and started a whole new life and started over with my career, I dealt with some more health issues and it was like a light switch.

I went to bed 1 night and I was up all night. This was nuts. Like my mind and body wouldn't shut off. This was the start of my hell of 16 years of Insomnia. Deep depression around the same time, I don't know which came 1st but all the more reason for meds right!?!? Doctor put me on FIVE different meds at this time. I was a ZOMBIE. I couldn't think, or function and was at my lowest weight at just under 100 lbs. I almost killed my dog (I let my dog outside sometime in the middle of the night in the dead of winter) because of the medication complications I had. I would get up in the middle of the night and do things and not know it.

Gonna fast forward to about 10 years ago now or so when I became severely sick. I started losing my voice randomly, feeling fine but no voice. Then I would get sick with EVERYTHING. I wasn't sleeping even with the meds and my brain was so exhausted as was my body. I progressed into getting a distended stomach when I would eat and it didn't seem to matter what.

Eye swelling too, oh and forgot all the allergy issues I had. Allergy testing, meds (of course!), and those now were no longer working either. NO ONE knew why I was having these issues. I went from medical doctor to doctor, and dermatologist. Now I was on my way to a full blown ulcer. I was in a constant decline. They biopsied 4 spots on my stomach and removed a polyp that I didn't know that I had.

I was seeing a gastro specialist at this time and he wanted me to take even more meds! He also wanted me to stop any alternative natural treatments that I was exploring, and I looked at him and said "HELL NO! You guys got me here and I am done being medicated."

I then ended up being referred to see a friend's wife who did Bio-Feedback. I had nothing to lose at this point. So then follows a couple years I believe of me doing Biofeedback and Foot Detoxes to get "better".

I got "better" for several years but then more stress struck (family/friend deaths, some trauma and life). I was still taking meds for sleeping (on and off), and was diagnosed with a mood disorder as well which meant more meds. It is funny to see that when you write this all out and journal your thoughts, you really do see how long it's been that you've been poisoned for and that's not even including the vaccines and antibiotics taken through all the years.

I then started gaining weight and this made no sense as I had always been a "clean eater". Many rounds of being tested for Thyroid issues followed and they said I'm fine!? When I got so sick the 1st time they wanted me off the birth control pill because they said that can cause issues. Strange, I don't remember anyone telling me this in all the years I was on it. I didn't like being on it but couldn't be without because of the severity of the pain. So I got off it.

Moving on, I then was feeling exhausted again, laid out when I ate and with a distended stomach again. Gas, bloating and pain. Things start to spiral down slowly but surely and I'm trying to hold onto the life I don't want to lose as I'm now taking pre-workouts just to make myself function throughout the days.

I crashed hard. I went from this super active person to not being able to physically push myself up off the floor or make it through more than 1 client if I was lucky. Chest racing was constant at this time too, labored breathing and anxiety through the roof. Brain fog, no memory, short or long. I didn't want to have to get dressed in the mornings.The physical ability it took to do this was astounding. There were so many symptoms at this time it's hard to list them all. I know many can relate who have dealt with Adrenal Fatigue themselves. It's a living nightmare. Just a completely miserable person to be around and I knew it but I had zero control over any of it. I needed help so badly but people leave when they can't understand. I ended up going at this pretty much on my own until I found an Adrenal Group whom I credit to really saving me at my very worst. Had I not had people who understood me, with the information to help me understand what the heck was all going on, I really don't know if I would still be here. Finding likeminded people is definitely a game changer.

I then came across the raw vegan, fruit and vegetable healing protocol and my world changed so much for the better after this. I learned day after day more and more and decided I was done with medical doctors, and I jumped on the fruits and herbs, what I like to call the Detox Train and I have never looked back. I continued on with Biofeedback and foot detoxes as well because each 1 of these pieces played their own role.

If I can come out of stage 3 adrenal dysfunction, dysbiosis, hormone imbalances, 16 years of insomnia, mood disorder, hypothyroidism, kidney failure, anxiety, depression, and IBS then you damn well better believe that anybody can make it out of their health challenges.

You have no idea the lives you will change just by telling 1 or 2 other people about your healing journey and that then spins into dozens and hundreds because when people hear you and where you've come from, they know and have the mental strength to say "You know what, they are right!"

The lessons I value most from my journey are:

1. Changing your diet... MATTERS.

2. Taking herbs over supplements... MATTERS.

3. Dealing with mental, emotional junk we've stuffed... OH SO MATTERS.

4. Truly educating yourselves on the body and how detox works.. MATTERS.

5. Understanding it takes more than 1 thing to "fix" you... MATTERS.

6. Doing more than 1 thing at a time... MATTERS.

7. Getting that it's a process... MATTERS.

8. Knowing you didn't get this way overnight and having grace with yourself... MATTERS.

Keep getting educated and expanding your knowledge. Keep moving in the direction your body is telling you and just listen closely to it. There's many modalities that will help we just have to embrace them and be open. I hope this helps people relate and feel inspired. I have come a long way but my story is far from over."

Success Story #11: My Story So Far

"I have a short story for my progress so far in my early stages of detox and regeneration. I have mainly been transitioning since the last 2 months with some drops off the wagon...but I keep getting back on and keep going (it's key).

I am on a full fruit and herbal protocol during this time which has been my saving grace since my diet wasn't perfect for detoxing. So far - my kidneys started filtering, my adrenal glands have improved and I know this because I'm not tired all the time and I don't get drained from work as much as I used to. I have reduced my asthma prevention medication to half (I am on the lowest dose level, and taking half of that). No more Anxiety which was huge for me as I couldn't handle the bus, and work was a struggle.

I still feel some mild issues but I feel strong now that I can overcome the smaller stuff. The healing journey continues but so far, so good."

In the next volume, we will be discussing the main herbs that we have used and had much success with as part of the raw vegan healing protocol. We have found herbs to be extremely helpful in both the detoxification and regeneration stages.

Until next time, wishing you all the best.

Our Story

It was a Sunday night, over 7 years ago – I was in bed – tossing and turning – unable to sleep. I watched the time pass, from 11pm, to 12am… to 1:30am. I just couldn't sleep. I could feel an immense pressure in my chest cavity and all across my diaphragm area. I couldn't understand where this was coming from. I got up and had some water, I then tried to use the bathroom – the discomfort was still there. Nothing seemed to work – I felt like I was being suffocated each time I would lie down. In the end, I fell asleep out of sheer fatigue.

At the time, I was a sufferer of asthma, eczema, anxiety attacks, and a damaged/leaky gut. These conditions had lead to many symptoms that doctors could not offer me any answers for. I had many tests done but nothing could tell me what the root causes of my problems were.

I started researching about my symptoms, and as I did this, I found myself expanding into the area of medical history. As my research continued, I came to understand that our ancestors lived healthy and long lives, without the health challenges of today.

Eventually, I stumbled upon a few health forums which I joined. Through these, I met a series of individuals that were battling a variety of conditions themselves (a rare genetic disorder, Crohn's disease, multiple sclerosis, muscular dystrophy (MD), diabetes, cushing's disease, a series of 'incurable' autoimmune diseases, and cancer).

We all came together and as we started to grow as a group, we made a significant discovery - that actually the cure to all diseases was discovered back in the 1920s by a Dr Arnold Ehret.

As we studied his material, we started applying his information and protocols on ourselves. This seemed like one experiment worth trying, and within 2 weeks, regardless of our individual conditions, we all started to notice a difference in our improved digestion, higher energy levels, increased mental clarity and improved physical ability. A major change was taking place – our health was improving, as our conditions were decreasing.

We continued to expand our knowledge and we started to encounter even more communities and learnt that there were more magnificent and very gifted healers out there. We came across the works and achievements of Dr Sebi, and completed an insightful and very informative course by Dr Robert Morse.

The essential message of these great healers was very similar to that of Dr Arnold Ehret. Now we had even further confirmation that the information we had been following thus far was in fact THE path to health success. With our progress so far, we could sense victory.

Within 3 months, 30 to 40 percent of our symptoms had disappeared and our health was becoming stronger. Some of us started to take specific herbs in order to enhance the detoxification.

Another 3 months on and the majority of us no longer experienced any more symptoms. Our blood work had also improved significantly, but we still had work to do in order to completely heal.

Now that we had made significant progress in reversing our conditions through self-experimentation, we started to offer basic healthy eating advice to the sick within our local communities.

Eventually, we started working with local patients on a voluntary basis. It was heartbreaking to witness lives being cut short or chronic sickness being accepted as a way of life – all whilst the lifelong eating habits of these individuals remained. The most common diseases that we were coming across included: cancers, heart disease, chronic kidney disease, high blood pressure, varying infections, and diabetes.

By helping our communities with changing their daily eating habits, we started seeing results, and although the transitional phase of moving from the foods that they were so used to eating, to moving over to a raw plant-based routine was a challenge, in the end, it was worth the shift. Note: there were many that ignored our advice and sadly they continued to remain in their state.

We did have resistance initially from family members and friends of the sick but after some time as they started seeing health improvements, more started joining us, and they also started experiencing what we had when we first set out on our journey of natural self-healing.

Nevertheless, challenges still remained – the main ones being the undoing of society's programming that cooked food is an essential part of life (including animal and wheat based products) and raw food alone surely cannot be good for you. It doesn't take long to explain how to remove imbalances and dis-ease from within the human body but the more extensive task is to actually have the protocol information applied and adhered to completely.

This is where the idea for this series of journal & progress tracker stemmed from. We felt compelled to spread this information in a more digestible and applicable form, over a series of volumes, in which we would start by offering some key informative points, followed by a journal which would allow for you to actually apply the information, record your progress, daily feelings and stay accountable to yourself. We also found that journaling and writing to oneself really helps to self-motivate and enhances a self consciousness that is needed when following a protocol like this.

Each journal volume within this series will be designed to help you record your journey for a 30 day period. At the start of each journal we will continue to offer insightful information about our experiences, whilst expanding on and re-iterating specific parts of this protocol.

The fact that you are reading this foreword is an indication that you are already on your way to self-healing. Regardless of your condition, we invite you to seek more knowledge and set your health free.

May you always remain blessed and guided.

Much Love From The Health Central Team

Important Notes for Overcoming Your Heart Failure

1. It should be noted that based on our experiences and understanding, whether your condition is Heart Failure, or any other, we recommend the same raw vegan healing protocol across all spectrums. With some conditions, you may need to perform a deeper detoxification (using herbs - or organ/glandular meat/capsules for more chronic situations) before achieving significant results, but in general, we have found this protocol to work in most cases. In our experience, the goal is not to cure, but instead to raise health levels first, through healthy food choices, as intended for our species – before the eradication and prevention of these modern-day "disease" conditions can take place.

2. With all conditions, we have found that the lymphatic system has become congested and overwhelmed due to the kidneys not efficiently filtering out the accumulated cell waste – as a result of years of dehydrating cooked/ wheat/dairy foods. The adrenal glands work closely with the kidneys, and so adrenal/kidney herbs and glandular formulas played a major role in opening up these channels. We also found that opening up the bowels and loosening the gut was hugely important too.

3. The healing protocol that we used on ourselves is discussed and expanded upon throughout the various volumes in this series. Our goal is to share information that we have gathered from our journeys, and let you decide if it is something that you feel could also work for you in your

journey for health and vitality. You are not obliged to use this information, and you may proceed as you see fit.

Through our study, research and application, we have found this system to correct any internal imbalances and remove dis-ease that has occurred within the human body, due to the continued consumption of acid-forming foods.

4. Always take progression ultra slow and go at your own pace. Listen to your body at every stage. We cannot re-iterate this point enough. Pay attention to how you feel and continue to consult your doctor and monitor your blood work.

5. A special emphasis needs to be given to the transition phase when moving from your regular, standard diet, to a raw vegan diet that is high in fruit. You must take your time and slowly remove foods from your current routine, and replace them with either fasting or a small amount of fruit in the initial stages. Work with small amounts – please do not make any drastic changes. If you do not feel comfortable or have any concerns at any stage, please immediately stop.

Note: with any dietary change, this can be a stressful event for the body and so it is important that you support your kidneys and adrenal glands using the appropriate herbs and glandular formulas previously mentioned.

6. Before partaking in any new dietary routine, please always consult your Doctor first and ensure that they are aware of your health related goals. This approach is beneficial because (a) you can monitor your blood work with your doctor as you progress with this new protocol, and (b) if you are on any medication, as your health improves, you

can review its need and/or discuss having dosage amounts reduced (if necessary).

7. Please note that we are sharing information from our collective experiences of how we healed ourselves from a variety of diseases and conditions. These are solely our own opinions. Having reversed a range of conditions using essentially the same protocol, our understanding and conclusion, based on our experience alone, is that regardless of the disease, illness or condition name – removing it from the human body stems from correcting your diet and transitioning over to a more raw vegan lifestyle.

8. Proceed with care, and again, do not make any sudden changes – always take your time in slowly removing foods that are not serving you, and replacing them with high energy sweet tree-ripened juicy fruit. If at any point you feel that you are moving too quickly, please adjust your transition accordingly. Results may vary between individuals.

9. We recommended that you constantly expand your knowledge and familiarise yourself with the works of Dr Arnold Ehret, Dr Robert Morse and John Rose. When you feel confident with your understanding, start taking gradual steps towards reaching your goals. Make the most of this journal and use it to serve you as a companion on your journey.

The Power of Journaling

a) Journaling your inner self talk is a truly effective way of increasing self awareness and consciousness. To be able to transfer your thoughts and feelings onto a piece of paper is a truly effective method of self reflection and improvement. This is much needed when you are switching to a high fruit dietary routine.

b) Be sure to always add the date of journaling at the top of each page used. This is invaluable for when you wish to go back and review/track progress and your feelings/thoughts on previous dates.

c) Keep a comprehensive record of activities, thoughts, and really log everything you ate/are eating. You can even make miscellaneous notes if you feel that they will help you.

d) We have added tips and questions to offer you guidance, reminders, inspiration and areas to journal about.

e) We like to use journals to have a conversation with ourselves. Inner talk can really help you overcome any challenges that you are experiencing. Express yourself and any concerns that you may have.

f) Try to advise yourself as though you are your best friend – similarly to how you would advise a close friend or family member. You will be surprised at the results that you will achieve from using this technique.

g) Add notes to this journal and work your way through the 30 days. Once completed, move onto the next journal volume in this series, which will also be structured in a similar, supportive and educational fashion. We have produced a series of these journals in order to cater for your ongoing journey and goals.

h) For those of you who would like to track your progress with a more basic notebook-style journal, we have produced a separate series in which each notebook interior differs. This is to cater for your complete health journaling needs.

We have laid out the following examples to serve as potential frameworks for one way of how a journal could be filled in on a daily basis. These are just basic examples, but you can complete your daily journals in any other way that you feel is most comfortable and effective for you.

[EXAMPLE 1]
Today's Date: 3rd Jan 2020

Morning

Dry fasting (water and food free since 8pm last night) - will go up until 12:30pm today, and start with 500ml of spring water before eating half a watermelon.

Afternoon

Kept busy and was in and out quite a bit – so nothing consumed.

Evening

At around 5pm, I had a peppermint tea with a selection of mixed dried fruit (small bowl of apricot, dates, mango, pineapple, and prunes).

Night

Sipped on spring water through the evening as required.
Finished off the other half of the watermelon from the morning.

Today's Notes (Highlights, Thoughts, Feelings):

As with most days, today started well with me dry fasting (continuing my fast from my sleep/skipping breakfast) up until around 12:30pm and then eating half a watermelon. The laxative effect of the watermelon helped me poop and release any loosened toxins from the fasting period.
I tend to struggle on some days from 3pm onwards. Up until that point I am okay but if the cravings strike then it can be challenging. I remind myself that those burgers and chips do not have any live healing energy.
I feel good in general. I feel fantastic doing a fruit/juice fast but slightly empty by the end of the day.
Cooked food makes me feel severe fatigue and mental fog.
Will continue with my fruit fasting and start to introduce fruit juices due to their deeper detox benefits. I would love to be on juices only as I have seen others within the community achieve amazing results.

[EXAMPLE 2]

Today's Date: 4th Jan 2020

Morning

Today I woke and my children were enjoying some watermelon for breakfast - and the smell was luring so I joined them. Large bowl of watermelon eaten at around 8am. Started with a glass of water.

Afternoon

Snacked on left over watermelon throughout the morning and afternoon. Had 5 dates an hour or so after.

Evening

Had around 3 mangoes at around 6pm. Felt content - but then I was invited round to a family gathering where a selection of pizzas, burgers and chips were being served. I gave into the peer pressure and felt like I let myself down!

Night

Having over-eaten earlier on in the evening, I was still feeling bloated with a headache (possibly digestion related) and I also felt quite mucus filled (wheez in chest and coughing up phlegm). Very sleepy and low energy. The perils of cooked foods!!

Today's Notes (Highlights, Thoughts, Feelings):

I let myself down today. It all started well until I ate a fully blown meal (and over-ate). I didn't remain focussed and I spun off track. As a result my energy levels were much lower and I felt a bout of extreme fatigue 30 minutes after the meal (most likely the body struggling to with digesting all that cooked food).
I need to stick to the plan because the difference between fruit fasting, and eating cooked foods is huge - 1 makes you feel empowered whilst the other makes you feel drained. I also felt the mucus overload after the meal - it kicked in pretty quickly.
Today I felt disappointed after giving in to the meal but tomorrow is a new day and I will keep on going! It is important to remind myself that I won't get better if I cannot stick to the routine.

1. Today's Date:

—————————— Morning ——————————
(work towards continuing your night time dry fast up until at least 12pm)

—————————— Afternoon ——————————
(get hydrating with fresh fruit or even better slow juiced fruits/berries/melons)

—————————— Evening ——————————
(aim to wind down to a dry fast by around 6pm to 7pm)

—————————— Night ——————————
(work your way up to dry fasting from the evening until 12pm the following day)

Today's Notes (Highlights, Thoughts, Feelings, What Could You Improve On?)

"Get yourself an accountability partner to complete a 30 day detox with. Start with 7 days and work your way up. It will be fun and motivating completing it with somebody (or a group) ...or of course you can go it alone."

2. Today's Date:

Morning
(work towards continuing your night time dry fast up until at least 12pm)

Afternoon
(get hydrating with fresh fruit or even better slow juiced fruits/berries/melons)

Evening
(aim to wind down to a dry fast by around 6pm to 7pm)

Night
(work your way up to dry fasting from the evening until 12pm the following day)

Today's Notes (Highlights, Thoughts, Feelings, What Could You Improve On?)

"Remember when starting out, it is important to keep yourself hydrated throughout the day. Spring Water is a good start - and slow/cold pressed juice is also very powerful."

3. Today's Date:

Morning
(work towards continuing your night time dry fast up until at least 12pm)

Afternoon
(get hydrating with fresh fruit or even better slow juiced fruits/berries/melons)

Evening
(aim to wind down to a dry fast by around 6pm to 7pm)

Night
(work your way up to dry fasting from the evening until 12pm the following day)

Today's Notes (Highlights, Thoughts, Feelings, What Could You Improve On?)

"Eat melons/watermelons separately, and before any other fruit as it digests faster and we want to limit fermentation (acidity) which can occur if other fruits are mixed in."

4. Today's Date:

Morning
(work towards continuing your night time dry fast up until at least 12pm)

Afternoon
(get hydrating with fresh fruit or even better slow juiced fruits/berries/melons)

Evening
(aim to wind down to a dry fast by around 6pm to 7pm)

Night
(work your way up to dry fasting from the evening until 12pm the following day)

Today's Notes (Highlights, Thoughts, Feelings, What Could You Improve On?)

"Stay focussed on the end goal of removing mucus & toxins from your body and feeling wonderful! Look forward to being full of vitality and disease free once again"

5. Today's Date:

Morning
(work towards continuing your night time dry fast up until at least 12pm)

Afternoon
(get hydrating with fresh fruit or even better slow juiced fruits/berries/melons)

Evening
(aim to wind down to a dry fast by around 6pm to 7pm)

Night
(work your way up to dry fasting from the evening until 12pm the following day)

Today's Notes (Highlights, Thoughts, Feelings, What Could You Improve On?)

"Meditate and perform deep breathing exercises in order to help yourself remain present minded and on track. Perform these techniques throughout the day but also during any challenging times that you may come to face."

6. Today's Date:

Morning
(work towards continuing your night time dry fast up until at least 12pm)

Afternoon
(get hydrating with fresh fruit or even better slow juiced fruits/berries/melons)

Evening
(aim to wind down to a dry fast by around 6pm to 7pm)

Night
(work your way up to dry fasting from the evening until 12pm the following day)

Today's Notes (Highlights, Thoughts, Feelings, What Could You Improve On?)

"Join a few like-minded communities – there are many juicing and raw vegan based groups, both online and offline. Being part of a community can help motivate you to reach your goals. You will also learn a great amount from others. Seeing others succeed is empowering."

7. Today's Date:

Morning

(work towards continuing your night time dry fast up until at least 12pm)

Afternoon

(get hydrating with fresh fruit or even better slow juiced fruits/berries/melons)

Evening

(aim to wind down to a dry fast by around 6pm to 7pm)

Night

(work your way up to dry fasting from the evening until 12pm the following day)

Today's Notes (Highlights, Thoughts, Feelings, What Could You Improve On?)

"If you are struggling to cope with hunger pangs in the early stages, try some dates or dried apricots, prunes, or raisins, with a cup of herbal tea. However, these pangs will disappear once your body adjusts to your new routine."

8. Today's Date:

Morning

(work towards continuing your night time dry fast up until at least 12pm)

Afternoon

(get hydrating with fresh fruit or even better slow juiced fruits/berries/melons)

Evening

(aim to wind down to a dry fast by around 6pm to 7pm)

Night

(work your way up to dry fasting from the evening until 12pm the following day)

Today's Notes (Highlights, Thoughts, Feelings, What Could You Improve On?)

"Get into a routine of regularly buying fresh fruit (or grow your own if weather permits) to keep your supplies up. Local wholesale markets do also clear fruits/veg on Fridays (if they are closed for the weekend) at a lower price, so they are worth a visit."

9. Today's Date:

Morning
(work towards continuing your night time dry fast up until at least 12pm)

Afternoon
(get hydrating with fresh fruit or even better slow juiced fruits/berries/melons)

Evening
(aim to wind down to a dry fast by around 6pm to 7pm)

Night
(work your way up to dry fasting from the evening until 12pm the following day)

Today's Notes (Highlights, Thoughts, Feelings, What Could You Improve On?)

"Regularly remind yourself about the great rewards and benefits that you will experience by keeping up this detoxification process. Imagine the lives you could save as a result of healing yourself."

10. Today's Date:

Morning

(work towards continuing your night time dry fast up until at least 12pm)

Afternoon

(get hydrating with fresh fruit or even better slow juiced fruits/berries/melons)

Evening

(aim to wind down to a dry fast by around 6pm to 7pm)

Night

(work your way up to dry fasting from the evening until 12pm the following day)

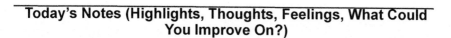

Today's Notes (Highlights, Thoughts, Feelings, What Could You Improve On?)

"Keep your teeth brushed (using miswak; a natural brush). Use coconut oil to oil pull before bedtime. Done correctly, you will notice an improvement in your dental health with these practices."

11. Today's Date:

Morning
(work towards continuing your night time dry fast up until at least 12pm)

Afternoon
(get hydrating with fresh fruit or even better slow juiced fruits/berries/melons)

Evening
(aim to wind down to a dry fast by around 6pm to 7pm)

Night
(work your way up to dry fasting from the evening until 12pm the following day)

Today's Notes (Highlights, Thoughts, Feelings, What Could You Improve On?)

"Be motivated by the vision of becoming an example for others to learn from and follow. You could change the lives of family and friends by showing them your own improvements."

12. Today's Date:

Morning
(work towards continuing your night time dry fast up until at least 12pm)

Afternoon
(get hydrating with fresh fruit or even better slow juiced fruits/berries/melons)

Evening
(aim to wind down to a dry fast by around 6pm to 7pm)

Night
(work your way up to dry fasting from the evening until 12pm the following day)

Today's Notes (Highlights, Thoughts, Feelings, What Could You Improve On?)

"Embrace your achievements and wonderful results – feel and appreciate the difference within you as a result of this new routine. Notice how your personal agility and fitness has improved. Feel the improved energy levels."

13. Today's Date:

Morning

(work towards continuing your night time dry fast up until at least 12pm)

Afternoon

(get hydrating with fresh fruit or even better slow juiced fruits/berries/melons)

Evening

(aim to wind down to a dry fast by around 6pm to 7pm)

Night

(work your way up to dry fasting from the evening until 12pm the following day)

Today's Notes (Highlights, Thoughts, Feelings, What Could You Improve On?)

*"Buy fruit in bulk where possible so you have
ample supplies for a week or two in advance.
If in a hot climate, you could even freeze your
fruit or make ice lollies out of it (crush & freeze).
Immerse yourself in fruit so it becomes your only option."*

14. Today's Date:

Morning
(work towards continuing your night time dry fast up until at least 12pm)

Afternoon
(get hydrating with fresh fruit or even better slow juiced fruits/berries/melons)

Evening
(aim to wind down to a dry fast by around 6pm to 7pm)

Night
(work your way up to dry fasting from the evening until 12pm the following day)

Today's Notes (Highlights, Thoughts, Feelings, What Could You Improve On?)

"Stay as busy as you can during the daytime. Creating a busy routine makes it easier to manage your diet. Have a purpose, and keep setting yourself new tasks/actions in order to keep yourself occupied."

15. Today's Date:

Morning

(work towards continuing your night time dry fast up until at least 12pm)

Afternoon

(get hydrating with fresh fruit or even better slow juiced fruits/berries/melons)

Evening

(aim to wind down to a dry fast by around 6pm to 7pm)

Night

(work your way up to dry fasting from the evening until 12pm the following day)

Today's Notes (Highlights, Thoughts, Feelings, What Could You Improve On?)

"Complete your fruit and fasting routine with a group of friends/family/colleagues so you can all support one another. Make it fun - set challenges - dry fast together and break your fasts together - have weekly catch up sessions."

16. Today's Date:

—————————— Morning ——————————
(work towards continuing your night time dry fast up until at least 12pm)

—————————— Afternoon ——————————
(get hydrating with fresh fruit or even better slow juiced fruits/berries/melons)

—————————— Evening ——————————
(aim to wind down to a dry fast by around 6pm to 7pm)

—————————— Night ——————————
(work your way up to dry fasting from the evening until 12pm the following day)

Today's Notes (Highlights, Thoughts, Feelings, What Could You Improve On?)

"Look out for white cloud/sediment (acids) in your urine to confirm that your kidneys are filtering out waste. Urinate in a glass jar - leave for 2 hours to settle before observing."

17. Today's Date:

Morning

(work towards continuing your night time dry fast up until at least 12pm)

Afternoon

(get hydrating with fresh fruit or even better slow juiced fruits/berries/melons)

Evening

(aim to wind down to a dry fast by around 6pm to 7pm)

Night

(work your way up to dry fasting from the evening until 12pm the following day)

Today's Notes (Highlights, Thoughts, Feelings, What Could You Improve On?)

"Have genuine love and care for yourself. If you are craving junk food, affirm positive inner talk ("I won't feel good after eating junk. I love myself too much to put my body through that - so leave it out!"). You can also take Sea Kelp, Coconut Water, or Celery to reduce any salt cravings."

18. Today's Date:

Morning
(work towards continuing your night time dry fast up until at least 12pm)

Afternoon
(get hydrating with fresh fruit or even better slow juiced fruits/berries/melons)

Evening
(aim to wind down to a dry fast by around 6pm to 7pm)

Night
(work your way up to dry fasting from the evening until 12pm the following day)

Today's Notes (Highlights, Thoughts, Feelings, What Could You Improve On?)

"Feel and note down the difference within yourself as you filter out unwanted acids with this alkaline, water-dense high fruit protocol."

19. Today's Date:

Morning

(work towards continuing your night time dry fast up until at least 12pm)

Afternoon

(get hydrating with fresh fruit or even better slow juiced fruits/berries/melons)

Evening

(aim to wind down to a dry fast by around 6pm to 7pm)

Night

(work your way up to dry fasting from the evening until 12pm the following day)

Today's Notes (Highlights, Thoughts, Feelings, What Could You Improve On?)

"Look for acidic waste/sediments in your urine regularly in order to ensure your kidneys are filtering. Dry fasting for over 18 hours will increase kidney filtration. You can also drink the juice of slow-juiced citrus fruits (lemons, oranges). Sweating helps too."

20. Today's Date:

Morning
(work towards continuing your night time dry fast up until at least 12pm)

Afternoon
(get hydrating with fresh fruit or even better slow juiced fruits/berries/melons)

Evening
(aim to wind down to a dry fast by around 6pm to 7pm)

Night
(work your way up to dry fasting from the evening until 12pm the following day)

Today's Notes (Highlights, Thoughts, Feelings, What Could You Improve On?)

"Infections emerge in an acidic environment. In order to remove infections, you must concentrate on kidney filtration. Use herbs for kidneys and adrenal glands - using dry fasting to assist."

21. Today's Date:

Morning
(work towards continuing your night time dry fast up until at least 12pm)

Afternoon
(get hydrating with fresh fruit or even better slow juiced fruits/berries/melons)

Evening
(aim to wind down to a dry fast by around 6pm to 7pm)

Night
(work your way up to dry fasting from the evening until 12pm the following day)

Today's Notes (Highlights, Thoughts, Feelings, What Could You Improve On?)

"Any deficiencies that you may have will start to disappear once you have cleansed your congested gut/colon, kidneys and various other eliminative organs."

22. Today's Date:

Morning
(work towards continuing your night time dry fast up until at least 12pm)

Afternoon
(get hydrating with fresh fruit or even better slow juiced fruits/berries/melons)

Evening
(aim to wind down to a dry fast by around 6pm to 7pm)

Night
(work your way up to dry fasting from the evening until 12pm the following day)

Today's Notes (Highlights, Thoughts, Feelings, What Could You Improve On?)

"Dependant on how deeply you detoxify yourself, it is possible to eliminate any genetic weaknesses that you may have inherited. This will require a deep detoxification process which involves juicing your fruits with prolonged periods of dry fasting"

23. Today's Date:

Morning

(work towards continuing your night time dry fast up until at least 12pm)

Afternoon

(get hydrating with fresh fruit or even better slow juiced fruits/berries/melons)

Evening

(aim to wind down to a dry fast by around 6pm to 7pm)

Night

(work your way up to dry fasting from the evening until 12pm the following day)

Today's Notes (Highlights, Thoughts, Feelings, What Could You Improve On?)

"Stay focused on your detoxification for deeper, lasting results. All past injuries / trauma are also repairable for good. Get those old acids out and replace them with a pain-free alkaline environment"

24. Today's Date:

Morning
(work towards continuing your night time dry fast up until at least 12pm)

Afternoon
(get hydrating with fresh fruit or even better slow juiced fruits/berries/melons)

Evening
(aim to wind down to a dry fast by around 6pm to 7pm)

Night
(work your way up to dry fasting from the evening until 12pm the following day)

Today's Notes (Highlights, Thoughts, Feelings, What Could You Improve On?)

---

*"If you suffer from ongoing sadness / depression, a deep detox will support your mental health. You will soon notice a positive change in your mood. **Note:** you will need to support your adrenal glands and kidneys with glandulars and/or herbs (liqorice root, sea kelp, uva ursi, nettle)"*

---

25. Today's Date:

Morning

(work towards continuing your night time dry fast up until at least 12pm)

Afternoon

(get hydrating with fresh fruit or even better slow juiced fruits/berries/melons)

Evening

(aim to wind down to a dry fast by around 6pm to 7pm)

Night

(work your way up to dry fasting from the evening until 12pm the following day)

Today's Notes (Highlights, Thoughts, Feelings, What Could You Improve On?)

"Have your fruits/ juices throughout the day - with dry fasting gaps of at least 3 hours in-between each feed. As the evening approaches, start to dry fast fully – from this point on, your body wants to rest and heal."

26. Today's Date:

Morning
(work towards continuing your night time dry fast up until at least 12pm)

Afternoon
(get hydrating with fresh fruit or even better slow juiced fruits/berries/melons)

Evening
(aim to wind down to a dry fast by around 6pm to 7pm)

Night
(work your way up to dry fasting from the evening until 12pm the following day)

Today's Notes (Highlights, Thoughts, Feelings, What Could You Improve On?)

"The kidneys dislike proteins but really appreciate juicy fruits like melons, berries, citrus fruits, pineapples, mangoes, apples, grapes. Witness the difference by replacing cooked foods and protein with fruits. Become the change."

27. Today's Date:

Morning
(work towards continuing your night time dry fast up until at least 12pm)

Afternoon
(get hydrating with fresh fruit or even better slow juiced fruits/berries/melons)

Evening
(aim to wind down to a dry fast by around 6pm to 7pm)

Night
(work your way up to dry fasting from the evening until 12pm the following day)

Today's Notes (Highlights, Thoughts, Feelings, What Could You Improve On?)

"Healing is very easy. There's no need to complicate it. Keep everything simple and you will see results. Concentrate on improving your level of health to a point where dis-ease is dissolved"

28. Today's Date:

—————————————— Morning ——————————————
(work towards continuing your night time dry fast up until at least 12pm)

—————————————— Afternoon ——————————————
(get hydrating with fresh fruit or even better slow juiced fruits/berries/melons)

—————————————— Evening ——————————————
(aim to wind down to a dry fast by around 6pm to 7pm)

—————————————— Night ——————————————
(work your way up to dry fasting from the evening until 12pm the following day)

Today's Notes (Highlights, Thoughts, Feelings, What Could You Improve On?)

"Keep your body in an alkaline and hydrated state as this is where regeneration takes place - and disease cannot continue to exist. You can achieve this through a raw fruits and vegetables diet (find your balance between the two)"

29. Today's Date:

Morning
(work towards continuing your night time dry fast up until at least 12pm)

Afternoon
(get hydrating with fresh fruit or even better slow juiced fruits/berries/melons)

Evening
(aim to wind down to a dry fast by around 6pm to 7pm)

Night
(work your way up to dry fasting from the evening until 12pm the following day)

Today's Notes (Highlights, Thoughts, Feelings, What Could You Improve On?)

"An enema with boiled water (cooled down) can support your detox. However this high fruit dietary protocol will encourage healthy bowel movement and this should be sufficient, unless if you are at a chronic stage."

30. Today's Date:

Morning
(work towards continuing your night time dry fast up until at least 12pm)

Afternoon
(get hydrating with fresh fruit or even better slow juiced fruits/berries/melons)

Evening
(aim to wind down to a dry fast by around 6pm to 7pm)

Night
(work your way up to dry fasting from the evening until 12pm the following day)

Today's Notes (Highlights, Thoughts, Feelings, What Could You Improve On?)

"You can have your iris' read by an iridologist that works with Dr Bernard Jensen's system. An Iris Diagnosis will offer you information on specific areas of weakness that pre-exist for you to focus on."

Printed in Great Britain
by Amazon

27542200R00051